Gasparilla

Coloring & Activity Book

ISBN: 978-1-945812-69-9 paperback

The Legend of Gasparilla!

José Gasparilla was a Spanish nobleman until the day he fell in love with the sea. He hopped aboard a ship and gathered all of his closest friends to join his pirate crew. As he sailed around the world, he used treasure maps to find buried riches. He found chests filled with gold coins, glittering beads, and colorful jewels.

One day, Gasparilla discovered a place filled with great hiding spots—Tampa Bay! He buried his treasures all around the bay area, and to this day, no one has found them.

Every year, the people of Tampa Bay celebrate with the Gasparilla Pirate Festival. Pirate ships parade through Tampa Bay, tossing beads and other treasures to people in the crowd. It's the one place where everyone can become a pirate for a day.

Circle the right answer

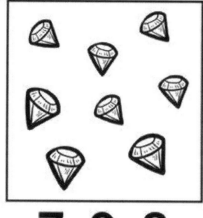

7 9 8

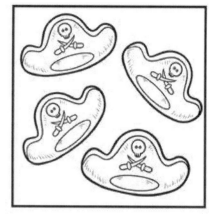

3 4 5

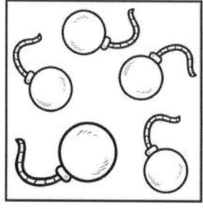

5 6 4

5 6 7

COLOR 1

CUT OUT 2

GLUE 3

USE EXAMPLE OR YOUR IMAGINATION

Find more fun children's books and additional types of novels from Richter Publishing LLC, a Tampa Bay publishing house, online here:

www.richterpublishing.com

Made in the USA
Columbia, SC
04 January 2019